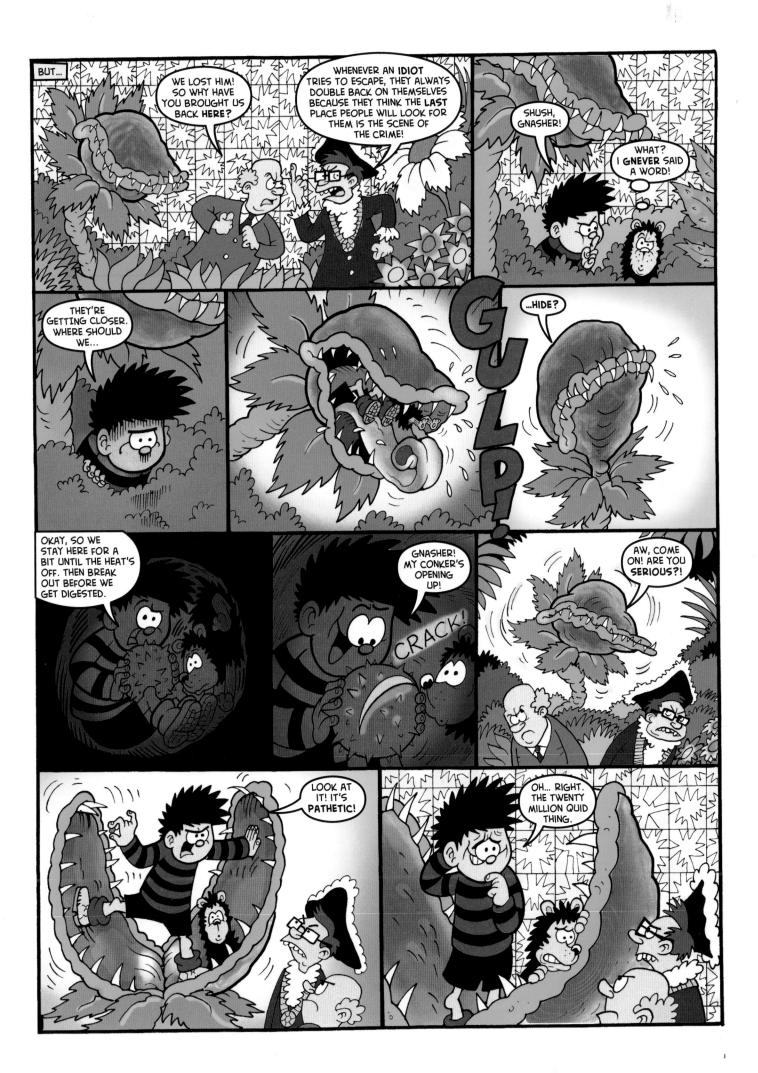

WHAT'S YOUR BEANO NAME?

EVERYBODY IN THE BEANO HAS A COOL NAME – DENNIS THE MENACE, MINNIE THE MINX, ROGER THE DODGER, TEACHER... WELL, OKAY – NOT **EVERYBODY**!

THERE'S AN EASY WAY TO FIND YOUR BEANO NAME. THE INITIAL OF YOUR FIRST NAME GIVES YOU THE FIRST HALF OF YOUR BEANO NAME. THEN THE MONTH YOU WERE BORN IN GIVES YOU THE SECOND HALF OF YOUR BEANO NAME. PUT THEM TOGETHER AND YOU ARE ALL BEANO'D UP!

MY BEANO NAME IS:

_____ THE _____

WHAT IS THE FIRST LETTER OF YOUR FIRST NAME?

EXTRA LARDY CRISPS

A: DOOMLORD
B: CATTY-MASTER
C: ROCKET SHOT
D: EGG-FLINGER
E: TOOTER
F: MASTERMIND
G: NOSE-PICKER
H: SCHEMER
I: WIZARD
J: BELCHER
K: BOOGIE
L: SNOOZY
M: BOTTOM
N: SNOT-RAG
O: TRUMPY-PANTS

P: SNORTER
Q: SHMOOPY
R: HAIRY-NOSE
S: BOGEY-MUNCHER
T: PLAN-MASTER
U: FUZZLE
V: GURU
W: GOOGLY
X: MARMALADE
Y: CHUFFER
Z: ZODIN

WHAT MONTH WERE YOU BORN IN?

JANUARY: THE MAGNIFICENT
FEBRUARY: THE BARBARIAN
MARCH: THE CRAFTY
APRIL: THE WARRIOR
MAY: THE MONSTER
JUNE: THE SLIGHTLY SMELLY
JULY: THE HORROR
AUGUST: THE DEVIOUS
SEPTEMBER: THE TERROR
OCTOBER: THE UNLIKELY
NOVEMBER: THE SNEAKY
DECEMBER: THE PRACTICAL JOKER

WORM JUICE

INK

ROGER THE DODGER

The Numskulls

THERE'S A LOT GOING ON IN EDD'S HEAD...

BRAINY IS PLANNING A TOUR OF THE LUNGS...

COME ON! YOU'VE GOT TO GO!

NO! I DON'T WANT TO!

BRAIN DEPT

YOU'RE IN CHARGE OF THE WHOLE BODY! SO YOU'VE GOT TO VISIT THE OTHER BITS OF IT SOMETIMES!

NO! STUFF ALWAYS GOES WRONG WHEN I LEAVE THE HEAD!

THE MOUTH DEPT...

OKAY - YOU GOT ME THIS FAR. I MAY AS WELL GO THE REST OF THE WAY.

IF YOU WAIT JUST A MOMENT MORE, EDD'LL BREATHE IN.

FOOD

AIR

ARRRGH!

GAL!!!

JUST LIKE THAT!

ARRRGH!

WHOOOOOSH!

THE LEFT LUNG...

ARRRGH!

WHO'S SCREAMING?

GUST!

ARRGH!

OH, IT'S JUST BRAINY!

HI, BRAINY!

POP!

BEFORE BRAINY LANDS, EDD BREATHES OUT AGAIN...

BYE, BRAINY!

SUCK!

BACK IN THE MOUTH DEPT...

THAT WAS QUICK!

DID YOU HAVE A NICE TIME?

WHERE'S HE GOING?

I'M NEVER LEAVING THE HEAD AGAIN! ARRRGH!

FOOD

AIR

BANANAMAN (MAN OF PEEL!)

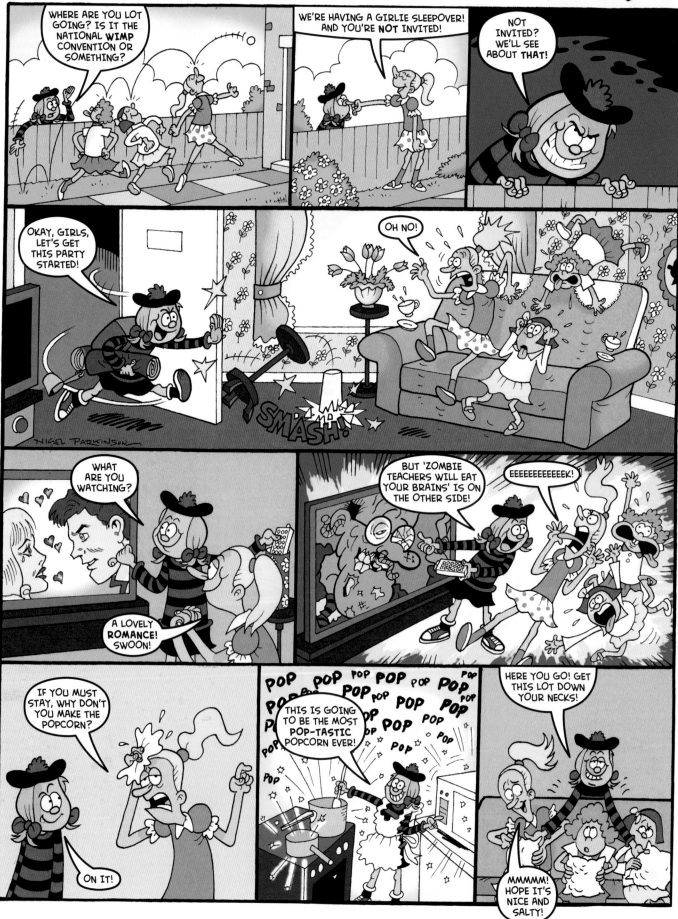

LITTLE PLUM

"I'VE GOT A **BIG** DELIVERY TOMORROW AND ONE OF THIS LOT ARE BOUND TO TRY AND **STEAL** IT."

WANTED

"DON'T WORRY, HANK. I'VE GOT AN IDEA."

NEXT DAY...

HANK'S STORE

PORRIDGE

"HYUK-HYUK! IT **LOOKS** LIKE BABY-FACE IS STEALING HANK'S DELIVERY..."

"...BUT IT'S REALLY ME IN DISGUISE!"

BFF

"BAH! BABY-FACE HAS BEATEN US TO IT!"

"NO PROBLEM. WE'LL JUST ROB HIS **HIDEOUT** INSTEAD."

BUT...

SECRET BANDIT'S HIDEOUT
proprietor: Baby-Face Finlayson

"EH? WHAT ARE YOU DOING HERE?"

"I LIVE HERE!"

"BUT WE JUST SAW YOU ROBBING HANK'S STORE!"

BACK AT HANK'S STORE...

"TWO BABY-FACES?! WE'VE BEEN HAD!"

LATER...

HANK'S STORE

SUGAR

"THANKS FOR HELPING ME, PLUM. THAT'S THE WHOLE DELIVERY **SAFE** FROM BEARS AND BANDITS!"

BUT...

HANK'S STORE

SUGAR

"THEY'VE DONE IT AGAIN!"

"THERE'S NO DISGUISING THAT!"

SUGAR

PUP PARADE

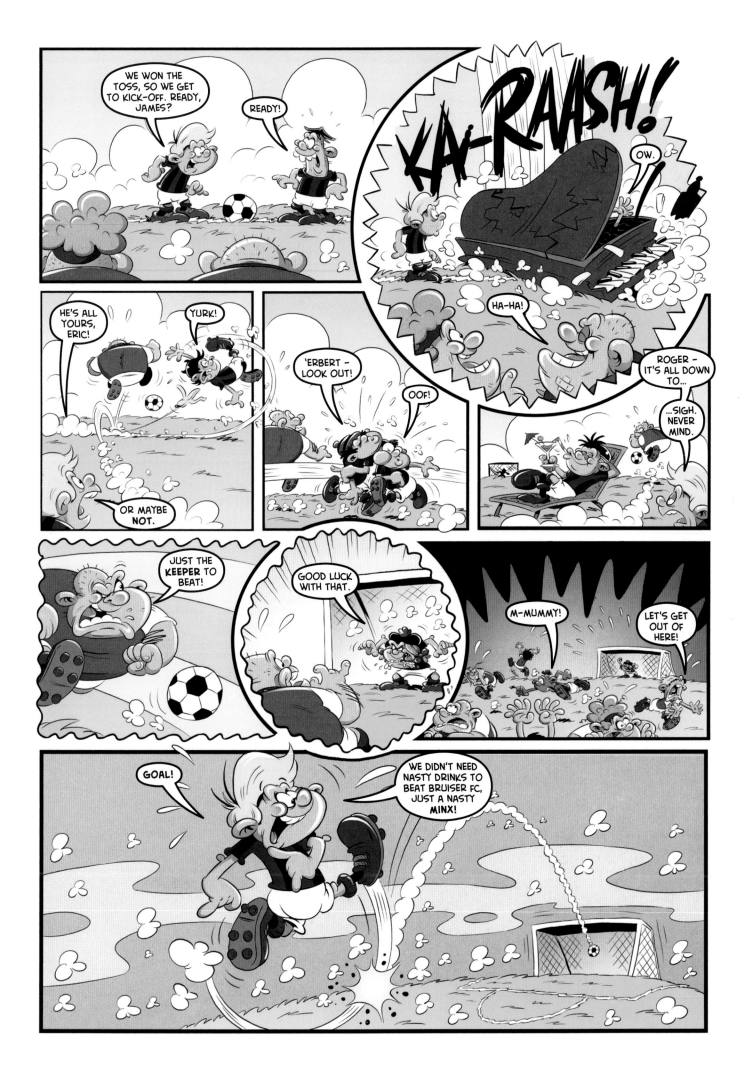

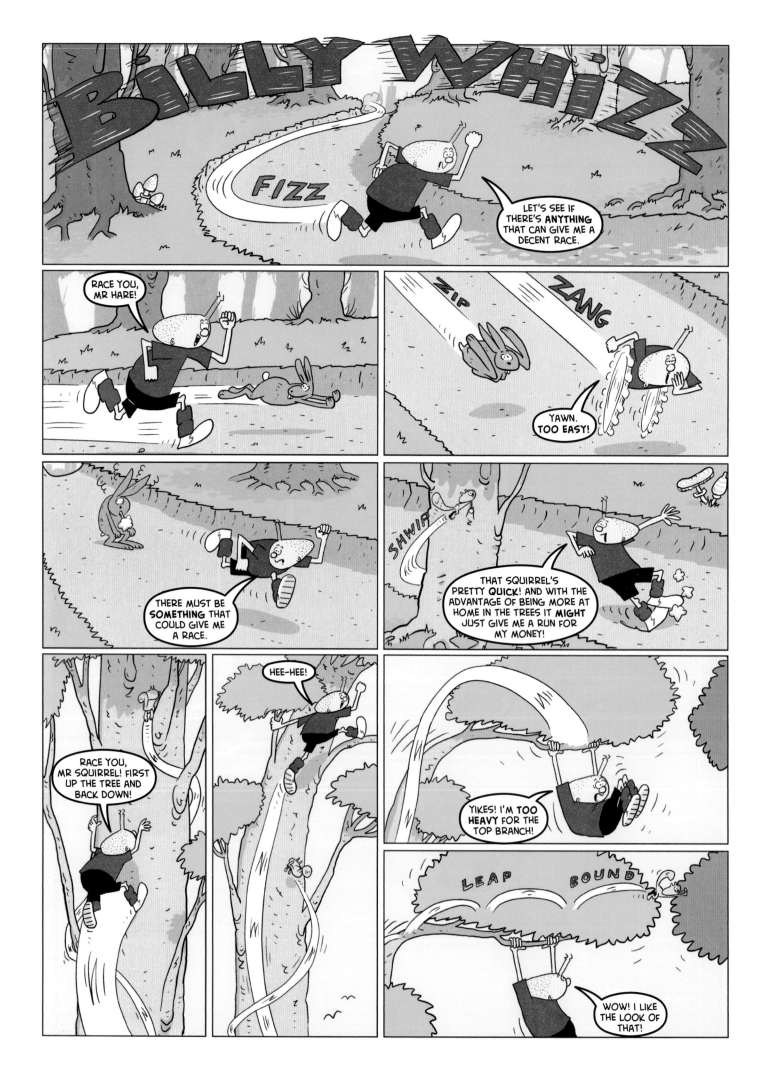

LES PRETEND

CONTINUED ON PAGE 59...

The Numskulls

THERE'S A LOT GOING ON IN EDD'S HEAD...

AT SCHOOL...

A CAR IS TRAVELLING AT 90 MILES AN HOUR TOWARDS A CASTLE 45 MILES AWAY...

...HOW LONG WILL THE JOURNEY TAKE?

THE BRAIN DEPT...

WHY'S EVERYONE LOOKING AT ME?

YOU'RE BRAINY!

BRAIN DEPT

IT'S SIMPLE MATHS. I JUST NEED TO PICTURE IT...

I'M DRIVING AT 90 MILES AN HOUR TOWARDS A CASTLE... BUT WHOSE CASTLE IS IT?

BRUM!

IT'S PROBABLY DRACULA'S CASTLE! WHY WOULD I DRIVE TOWARDS A PLACE LIKE THAT?

UNLESS...

...I'M TRYING TO RESCUE MY BEAUTIFUL WIFE! LET HER GO, YOU MONSTER!

HELP!

GRRR!

I GET THERE WITH MOMENTS TO SPARE AND VANQUISH THE EVIL CREATURE!

BRAIN DEPT

STAKE!

OW!

DUST!

BUT WE DON'T LIVE HAPPILY EVER AFTER...

...'COS THEN WE HAVE TO ESCAPE FROM FRANKENSTEIN'S MONSTER!

SO THE ANSWER MUST BE HALF AN HOUR.

IS IT? I'VE FORGOTTEN THE QUESTION.

THE BASH STREET KIDS

IN... LOST IN A GOOD BOOK!

Look – there he is! Teacher. I can see his lips moving, but I can't tell you what he's talking about. A book, I think. It's either that or he's describing the best way to fill the school toilets with custard. Actually, that one's probably my imagination.

I don't know how he does it, coming in here every day to try and teach us things we don't want to learn... uh-oh! I think he's just asked me a question.

"...I said – are you paying attention, Danny?"

"I think we both know the answer to that one, Sir," I replied. The other Bash Street Kids laughed. Yeah, that was a funny one.

"That was a funny one," Teacher agreed. "But what's even funnier is that you'll now be paying attention to me all over again in detention after school." Hmph – maybe not.

So here I am at three o'clock, stuck in class while the rest of the Bash Street kids are outside enjoying the sunshine. This hour of detention might just be the longest hour ever. Teacher places a chapter book on the desk in front of me. "Read it," he instructs me. I was wrong – this will definitely be the longest hour ever!

Only five minutes into the longest hour, I can already feel my eyelids getting heavier. I'm pretty sure I've read that last sentence three times already. That can't be good, can it? I know – I'll switch from resting my chin on my right hand to my left...

I sat up with a jolt! "I was just resting my eyes, Teacher," I said, before realising Teacher wasn't there. Nor was the desk, the classroom or Bash Street School! Instead, I seemed to be in a forest of some kind, surrounded by strangely shaped black trees. I walked around the nearest one. It stood taller than me, and the bark was smooth and black. Where had I found myself?

I called out. "Hello?"

"Hello," a familiar voice called back. It was Plug! Never have I been so pleased to see that ugly mug of his.

"You're a sore sight for eyes... um, sight for sore eyes," I told him.

"You're lost here too?" he asked. "Wherever here is."

"Is it just you? Or is everyone lost in this forest?"

"I dunno."

It didn't take long to find the whole gang - Fatty, Smiffy, 'Erbert, Wifrid, Spotty, Toots and Sidney. Having done so, the next thing to do was discover exactly where we were.

"It's an odd sort of forest," I said, touching the ground. "The ground is soft and white like pages of a book, and the trees are smooth and black. Think you could give me a leg up?"

With a little help from Plug, I was able to reach the top of the tree. The trees weren't actually trees! Well, not the leafy, climby, tree-housey kind. They all had letters instead of leaves, and each one spelled out a word! I told the guys.

"What word are you on?" Plug asked.

"Umm... cocoa."

Fatty's ears pricked up at the mention of his favourite thing. Well, I say favourite thing... it's more likely his joint favourite thing, along with curry, pizza, fish fingers, crisps, cola... where was I? Oh, yes - Fatty's ears! Or should I say Fatty's tongue? Fatty gave the word-tree a lick.

"What does the cocoa taste of?" asked Plug.

"You know when you chew your pen in class and it leaks everywhere? Kind of like that!"

Plug pulled a face at this. Um, I think... sometimes it's difficult to tell with Plug.

I hung from the edge of the word-tree and dropped back to the ground. "I can't see a way out," I confessed.

"Getting out is easy!" exclaimed Plug. I waited for him to explain. "Well?"

"Fine, thanks," he replied.

"I meant, well, aren't you going to share how we get out?"

"Oh. You have to defeat the master of this realm - Sir Prose!"

"How do you know that?"

"'Cos I'm not really here, Danny. I'm just part of your story."

I considered this revelation for a moment. And then I considered my use of the word revelation. It didn't sound like something I would say. Was I still in detention, reading? Or worse, learning new words from reading in detention? I came to a decision. "Prove it," I said.

It was daft Smiffy who took it upon himself to explain. "The square on the hippopotamus is the sum of the squares on the other two sides," he said proudly.

I burst out laughing. "Fair enough," I conceded. "Smiffy would never get as close to being right as that! So where do I find Sir Prose?"

"That's easy too," explained Plug. "He appears at the bottom of the page!"

"Surprise!" exclaimed Sir Prose.

Sir Prose looked just like Teacher! If Teacher played the part of D'Artagnan in the school production of The Three Musketeers, perhaps. He swished his cape across his shoulder with a flourish, showing of the glinting steel of the sword he carried in a belt at his waist.

"It is I, Sir Prose! I am the master of these pages, and what I say goes! Hee-hee! Look – I even managed a rhyming couplet there!"

The rest of the class laughed along with Sir Prose's joke. If I was in any doubt that these weren't my classmates, then I was absolutely sure now. I struck my most defiant pose.

"I challenge you to a duel, Sir Prose."

Sir Prose unclipped his cape, allowing it to fall to the floor.

"I accept."

He drew his sword, and swished the blade mere inches from the tip of my nose. It was close enough for me to be able to see my reflection in the polished metal. My reflection looked very scared despite my best efforts. I held up a finger.

"I don't suppose I could have one of these, could I? Ow!"

With only the gentlest movement from Sir Prose, the sword pricked the skin of my fingertip. Sir Prose laughed. "I don't need a sword to beat you. I can subordinate your conjuncts, restrict your clauses and predicate your adjectives without it!"

A spot of blood appeared on my finger – to my surprise it was blue! I thought it was only royalty that had blue blood! I gave it a quick lick. It was ink! An idea struck me.

"I know how I can put this land to writes!" I said with a boldness I did not feel.

"To rights? Pah!" scoffed Sir Prose.

"Nope! To writes!"

Using the ink from my fingertip on the paper pages on the earth below my feet, I quickly wrote, "Sir Prose could no longer hold in his enormous belly, filled as it was with tea and biccies! He exhaled with a gasp and the buttons on his britches popped one by one!

"No! Stop this!" cried Sir Prose in alarm.

Poor old Sir Prose tried to take a step, but with his britches round his ankles, all he could manage was a stagger. He fell forward, flattening his enormous conk! With Sir Prose defeated, The Bash Street Kids were set free from the pages of this rotten book and could go home at last!"

"Time to go home at last, Danny," said Teacher, glancing at his watch. My head snapped to attention at the sound of his voice. That's funny – that's exactly where my story ended too!

LES PRETEND

LITTLE PLUM

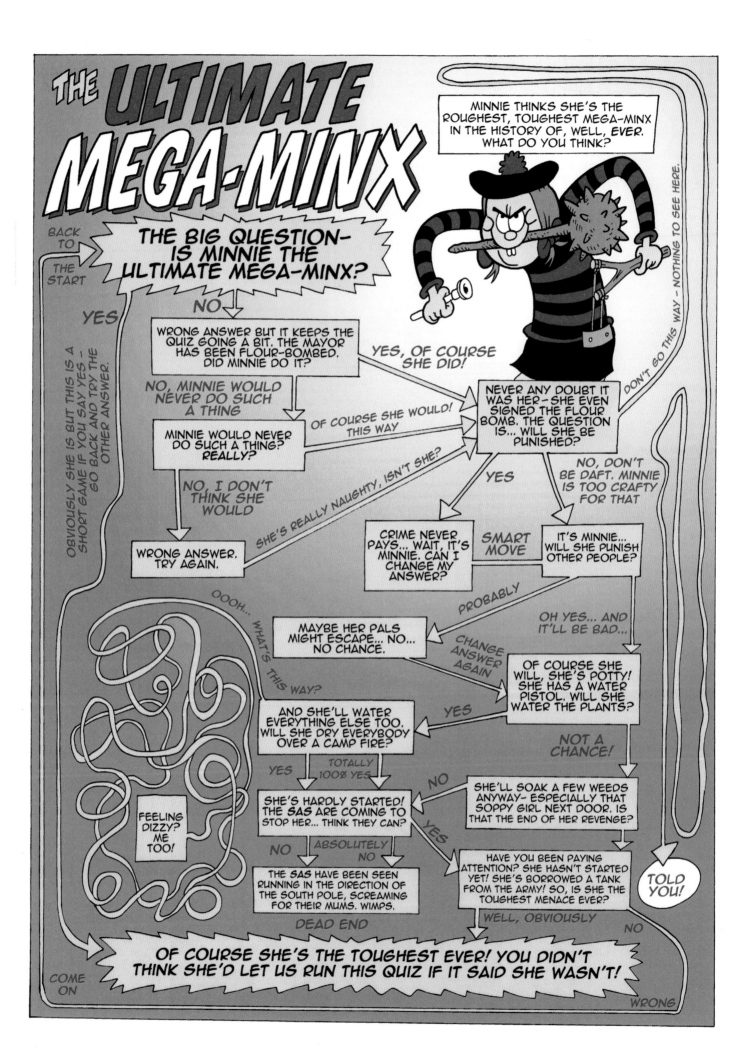

LORD SNOOTY

SCHOOL

HOME TIME! BEST TIME OF THE DAY!

AW... NOT THE GASWORKS GANG AGAIN!

IT'S SNOOTY! LET'S GET HIM!

WE WANT YOU TO BUY US SOMETHING, OR ELSE!

OR ELSE WHAT?

ER... DUNNO.

OR ELSE WE'LL SQUASH YOUR HAT, THAT'S WHAT!

YEAH! SO BUY US SOMETHING GOOD!

SO...

IS THIS GOOD ENOUGH FOR YOU?

WOW! OUR VERY OWN PRIVATE JET!

LET'S GO! WE CAN ORDER THE PILOT TO TAKE US ANYWHERE!

UH? NO PILOT? NO SEATS? WHAT'S GOING ON?

WAAHH! WE'RE TAKING OFF!

BUT THERE'S NO PILOT!

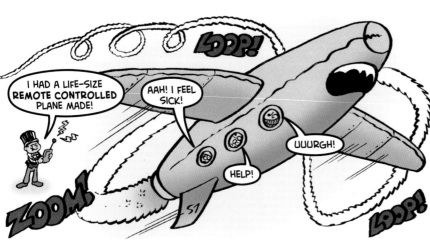

LOOP!

I HAD A LIFE-SIZE REMOTE CONTROLLED PLANE MADE!

AAH! I FEEL SICK!

HELP!

UUURGH!

ZOOM!

LOOP!

HA-HA! WHAT'S THE MATTER? DON'T YOU LIKE WHAT I BOUGHT FOR YOU?

GROAN! YOU CAN KEEP IT! IT SENT US LOOPY!

VISITING THE LOCAL TOY SHOP TO LOOK AT THE NEW ADVENTURE MAN TOYS, AN AVALANCHE OF TOYS KNOCKED GENERAL JUMBO TO THE GROUND.

GOODNESS! ARE YOU ALL RIGHT?

FINE, THANKS!

FORTUNATELY, JUMBO COULD REACH THE CONTROL DEVICE ON HIS WRIST.

GOT YOU.

MOMENTS LATER, TWO OF JUMBO'S REMOTE CONTROL HELICOPTERS ARRIVED IN THE SHOP.

WHERE DID **THEY** COME FROM?

USING THE HELICOPTERS' GRAPPLING HOOKS, JUMBO FREED HIMSELF FROM THE BOXES.

I'M SO TERRIBLY SORRY ABOUT THIS. I HAVE **NO** IDEA HOW THAT HAPPENED.

IT'S ALL RIGHT. I'M NOT HURT BADLY. JUST A BUMP ON THE HEAD.

UNFORTUNATELY FOR JUMBO, HIS DOCTOR PRESCRIBED A GOOD NIGHT'S REST TO GET OVER HIS ORDEAL.

WHAT KIND OF A GENERAL GETS SENT TO BED?

JUST A FEW HOURS LATER THE TOWN WAS ASLEEP, INCLUDING JONATHAN WILLIAMS WHO HAD TEASED JUMBO EARLIER.

BUT INSIDE THE HOUSE, NOT EVERYTHING WAS QUIET. MR WILLIAMS' WALL SAFE HAD BEEN DISCOVERED...

...AND OPENED.

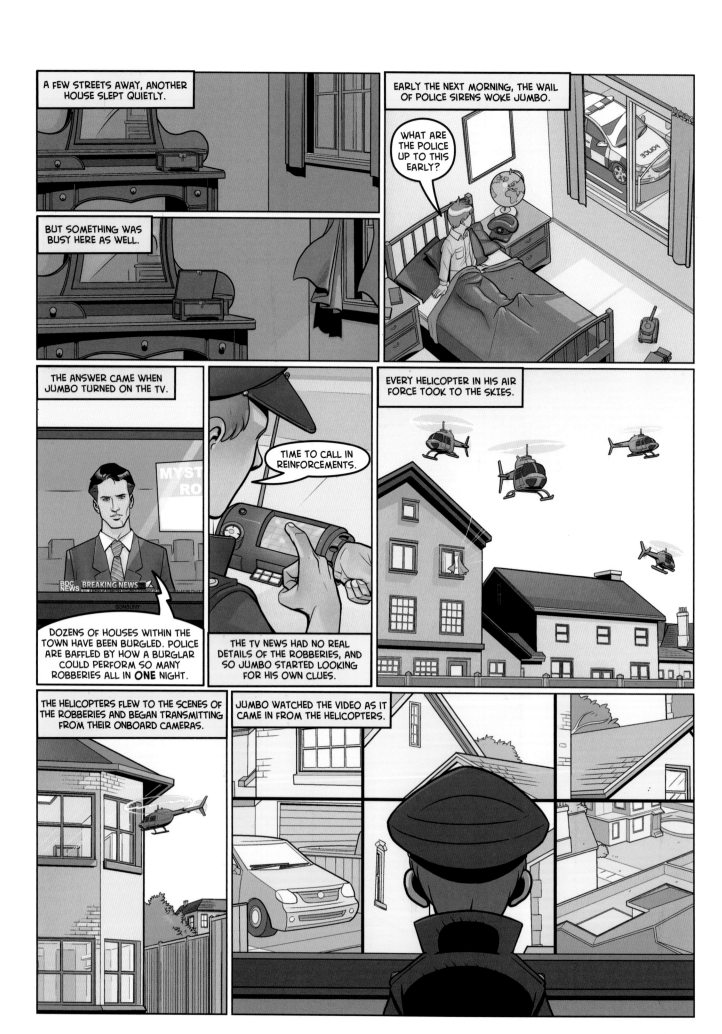

ROGER THE DODGER

THE ULTIMATE DODGE CODE

ONE OF THE MOST IMPORTANT BITS OF DODGING IS KEEPING SECRETS, SO IF YOU EVER HAVE TO WRITE SOMETHING DOWN, MAKE SURE NOBODY ELSE CAN READ IT BY USING ONE OF THESE SUPER SNEAKY DODGE CODES.

THE SLIDE CODE

WRITE OUT ALL THE LETTERS OF THE ALPHABET IN A LINE. THEN WRITE THE LETTERS OUT AGAIN, THIS TIME MOVING EVERY LETTER ALONG BY ONE LETTER SO IT LOOKS LIKE THIS...

A	B	C	D	E	F	G	H	I	J	K	L	M	N	O	P	Q	R	S	T	U	V	W	X	Y	Z
Z	A	B	C	D	E	F	G	H	I	J	K	L	M	N	O	P	Q	R	S	T	U	V	W	X	Y

WHEN YOU WRITE A MESSAGE, USE THE LETTERS UNDERNEATH.

ZKK SDZBGDQR RSHMJ!

___ _____ _____!

THE NUMBER CODE

MAKE SURE ALL YOUR FELLOW MENACES KNOW THESE CODES SO YOU CAN UNDERSTAND EACH OTHER'S MESSAGES!

AGAIN, WRITE ALL THE LETTERS ON THE ALPHABET IN A LINE.
UNDER EACH LETTER WRITE THE NUMBERS 1 TO 26 IN ORDER.

A	B	C	D	E	F	G	H	I	J	K	L	M	N	O	P	Q	R	S	T	U	V	W	X	Y	Z
1	2	3	4	5	6	7	8	9	10	11	12	13	14	15	16	17	18	19	20	21	22	23	24	25	26

WHEN YOU WANT TO SEND A MESSAGE, USE THE NUMBERS INSTEAD OF THE LETTERS.
LIKE THIS...

21, 19, 5, 1, 3, 1, 20, 1, 16, 21, 12, 20

___ _ _____ __

ROGER THE DODGER

The Numskulls

THERE'S A LOT GOING ON IN EDD'S HEAD...

BRAINY IS HARD AT WORK OPERATING EDD'S BRAIN...

FILM THIS ON YOUR PHONE, RADAR!

WE'RE IN CLASS AT THE MINUTE. SHOULDN'T WE...

JUST PRESS RECORD! I WANNA SEE HOW MUCH AIR I GET WHEN I DO AN OLLIE!

CRASH!

OOPS!

I GOT THAT, AND IT'S GOING ON YOUTUBE!

BUT...

OH NO! THE CONSOLE IS DAMAGED!

THE "RAISE RIGHT HAND" BUTTON IS STUCK ON!

I'LL UNSTICK IT BY HITTING IT MORE WITH THE SKATEBOARD!

BASH! BOSH!

THAT'S MADE IT WORSE! NOW THE "RAISE LEFT HAND" IS STUCK ON TOO!

I KNOW WHAT TO DO!

HIT IT SOME MORE!

BAM! BOSH! BASH!

DID THAT FIX IT?

IF BY "FIX" YOU MEAN "MAKE WORSE"...

OKAY, CAN ANYONE TELL ME THE ANSWER TO NUMBER SIX?

Dennis THE MENACE and GNASHER

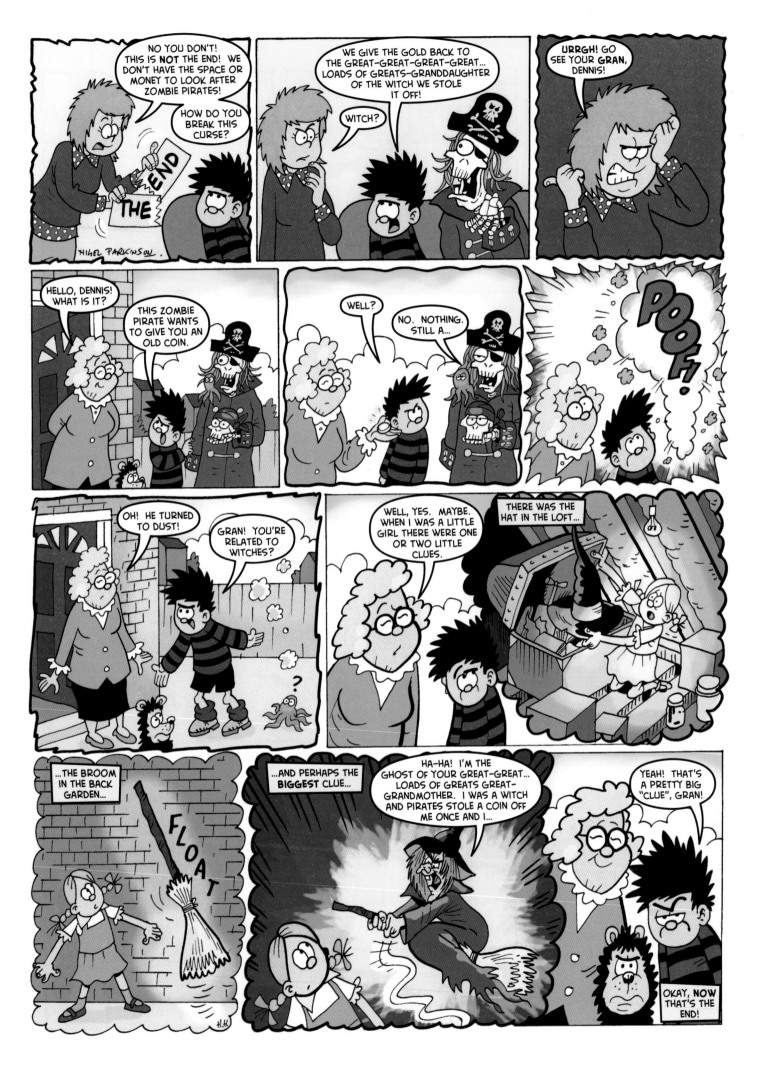

LUCKILY, JUMBO'S WRIST CONTROL CONTAINED A HISTORY OF ITS ACTIVITY, WHICH PROVED HIS ARMY HAD BEEN INACTIVE ALL NIGHT. IT PROVED JUMBO'S INNOCENCE

IT MUST HAVE BEEN YOU.

DON'T BE DAFT. WHY WOULD I SHOW YOU THE FOOTPRINTS IF I DID IT?

FAIR POINT, BUT YOU HAVE TO ADMIT IT'S SUSPICIOUS, JUMBO.

BUT IT MEANS SOMEBODY OUT THERE IS GUILTY. WHAT'S BEEN STOLEN?

MONEY... JEWELS... WHAT YOU'D EXPECT.

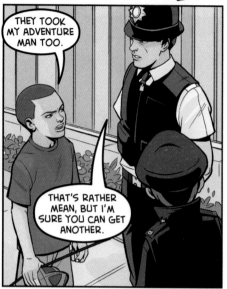

THEY TOOK MY ADVENTURE MAN TOO.

THAT'S RATHER MEAN, BUT I'M SURE YOU CAN GET ANOTHER.

I BET YOU'LL FIND THAT ALL THE OTHER ADVENTURE MEN HAVE GONE MISSING AS WELL. BUT THEY HAVEN'T BEEN STOLEN. THEY'RE THE THIEVES.

THAT'S ABSURD.

BUT PHONING THE OTHER CRIME SCENES, THE INSPECTOR FOUND THAT ALL OF THE TOYS HAD INDEED GONE MISSING.

WHAT? THE TOY VEHICLES ARE GONE AS WELL?

THAT MUST BE HOW THEY TRANSPORTED THE ADVENTURE MEN AND THE STOLEN GEAR AWAY.

SO WE'VE BEEN ROBBED BY TOYS? THAT'S A NEW ONE ON ME.

NOT TOYS. THEY'RE ADVANCED MACHINES, AND SOMEONE'S CONTROLLING THEM. BUT THERE MUST BE A SIGNAL BEING BROADCAST TO BRING THEM TOGETHER. IF THERE IS...

...I'VE GOT THE PLANE TO FIND IT! MY EARLY WARNING PLANE PICKS UP ALL KINDS OF RADIO SIGNALS.

GOT IT. THEY'RE ALL HEADING FOR THE COVE OUTSIDE OF TOWN.

WE'LL NEVER GET THERE IN TIME TO STOP THEM.

WE WON'T – BUT SOMEBODY WILL.

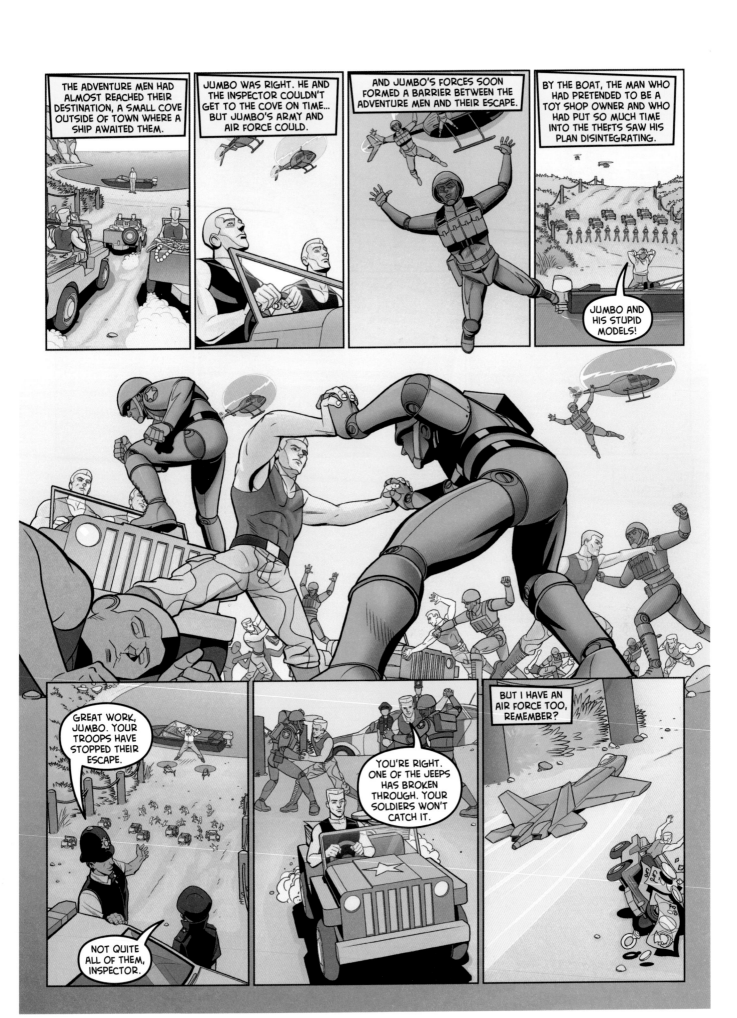

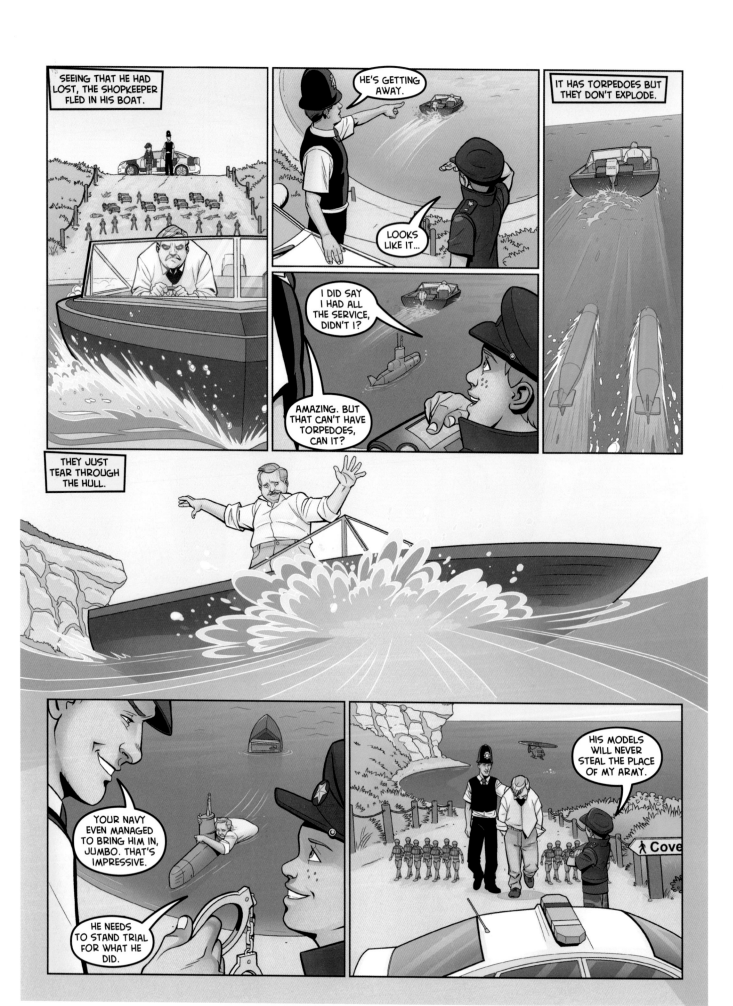

HMM! LOOKS LIKE WE MAY HAVE FOUND OUT WHERE ALL THE WATER HAS COME FROM.

I'M GOING IN!

THAT'S LUCKY! 'ERBERT'S HERE! ARF! ARF!

AH! THERE'S MY TOWEL!

EW! GROSS!

'ERBERT! YOU NEED TO TURN OFF THE TAPS... LIKE THIS!

YOU'RE SO FUNNY, DANNY!

TWEAK!

YEEOUCH!

AND SO...

COME ON IN, READERS, THE WATER'S LOVELY!

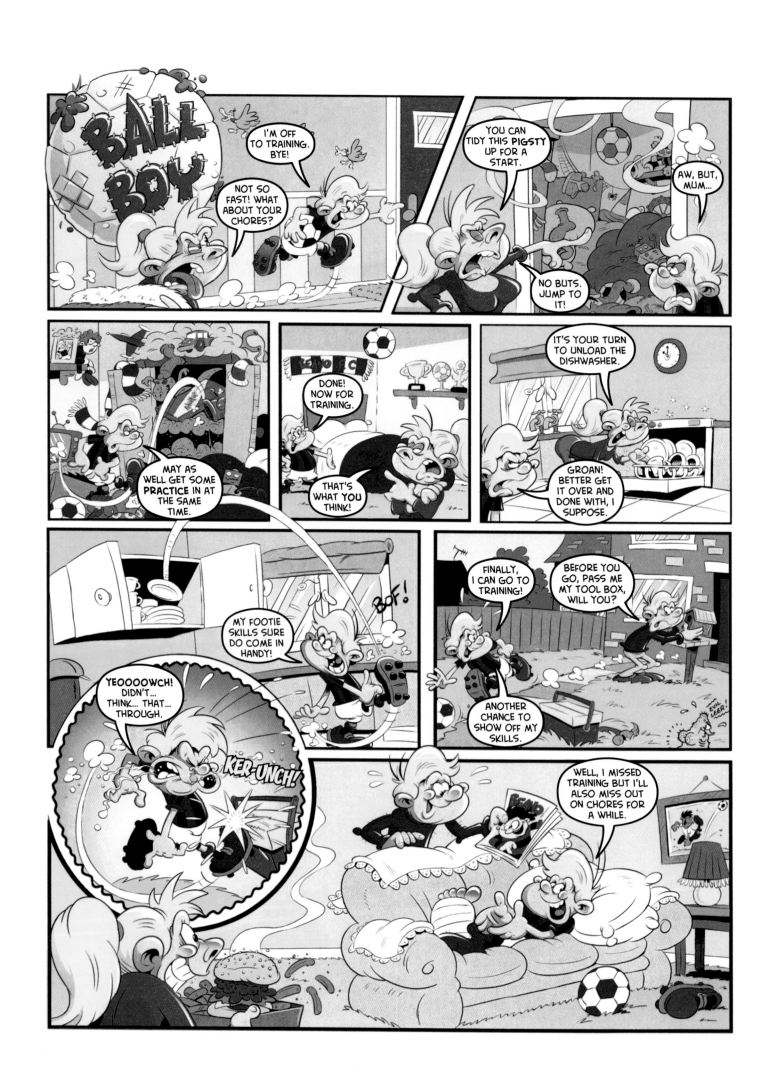

LITTLE PLUM

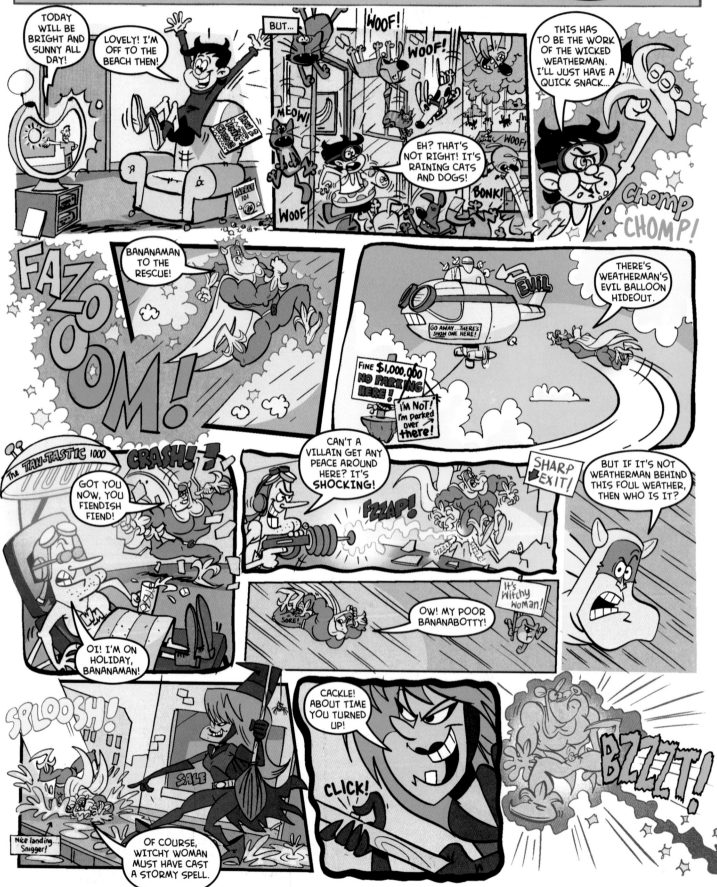

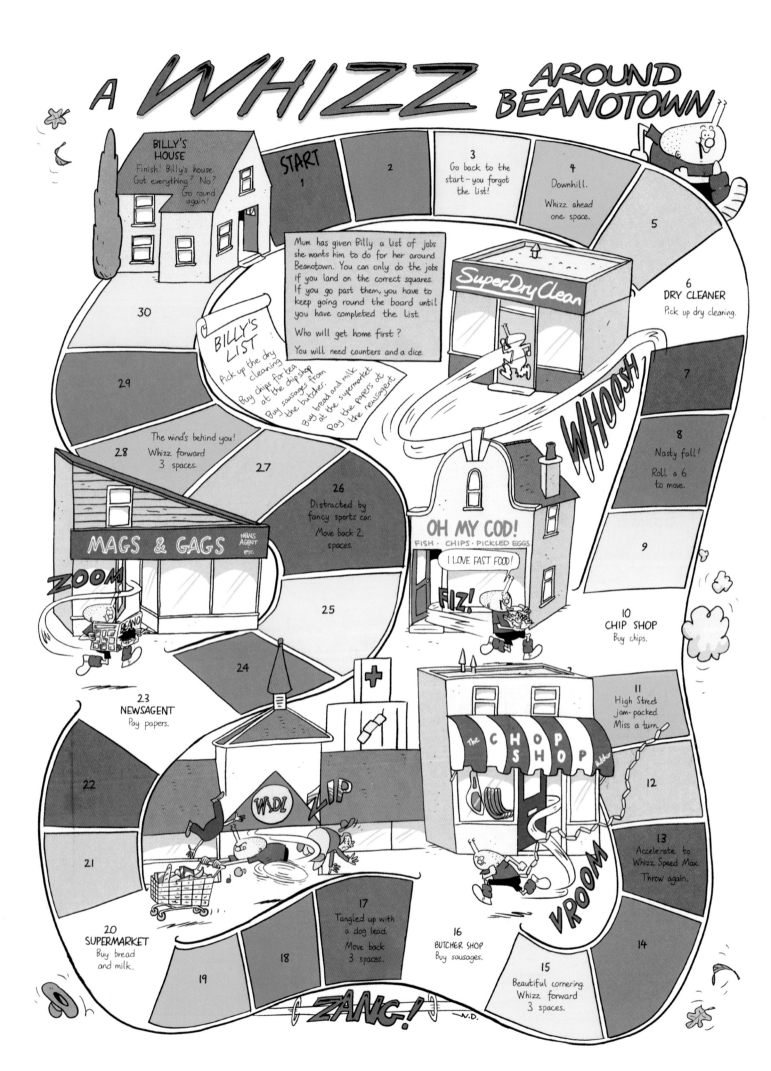

The Numskulls

THERE'S A LOT GOING ON IN EDD'S HEAD...

EDD HAS TO DO A BOOK REPORT...

SO IN THE BRAIN DEPARTMENT...

OKAY, GUYS. WE READ THIS BOOK. WAS IT ANY GOOD?

YES!

YES!

YES!

WHAT WAS GOOD ABOUT IT?

THE GOOD BITS.

YEAH, DEFINITELY THE GOOD BITS!

AND WHAT WAS BAD ABOUT IT?

THE BAD BITS?

YEAH, DEFINITELY THE BAD BITS!

OKAY. WHAT'S THIS BOOK CALLED?

ERM... BOOK?!

WHEN WE HAD THE BOOK OPEN AND WE HAD EDD'S EYES OPEN AND WE WERE TURNING PAGES, DID ANY OF US ACTUALLY **READ** THE WORDS?!

HARRUMPH! I THOUGHT AS MUCH!

OKAY! LET'S TRY AGAIN!

WE'RE DOING THIS TOGETHER, GUYS! EVERYONE READING?

EYE DEPT

YEAH!

YEAH!

TOTALLY READING!

THAT'S GOOD.

SO CAN ANYONE TELL ME WHY NONE OF YOU HAVE NOTICED THAT...

...THE BOOK'S UPSIDE DOWN!!

Chapter One
How it started

SWOT THE DIFFERENCE!

The Bash Street Kids are booby trapping the classroom but school swot, Cuthbert Cringeworthy is telling tales to Teacher! Can you swot... er SPOT the 10 differences between these two pictures?

ANSWER →

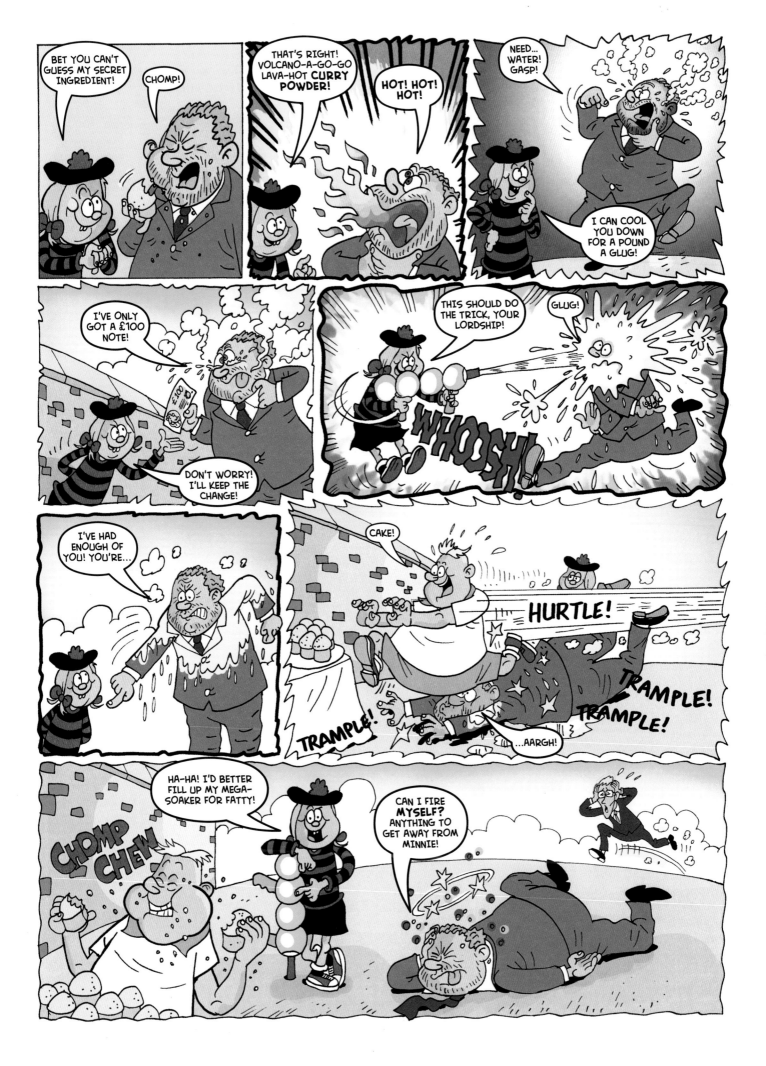

DO YOU KNOW YOUR SQUELCHIES?

THESE ARE THE TV & FILM SQUELCHIES

 Count Dracula

 Bugs

 Squelchy the Builder

 Frankensquelchy

 Casper

Mummy

 The Lone Squelchy

 Robin Hood

 Dalek

 Tinkerbell S

 Gordon Chef

 Biker

 Nurse

 PC

 Gnash

 Jester

 Zombie

 Gnome

 Tenor

 Harry Hill

 Woody

 Harry

 Postsquelch Pat

 Square Pants

 Captain Jack

 Mutant Ninja

 Power

 Squelchy in Black

 Sully

 Darth

Dennis THE MENACE and GNASHER

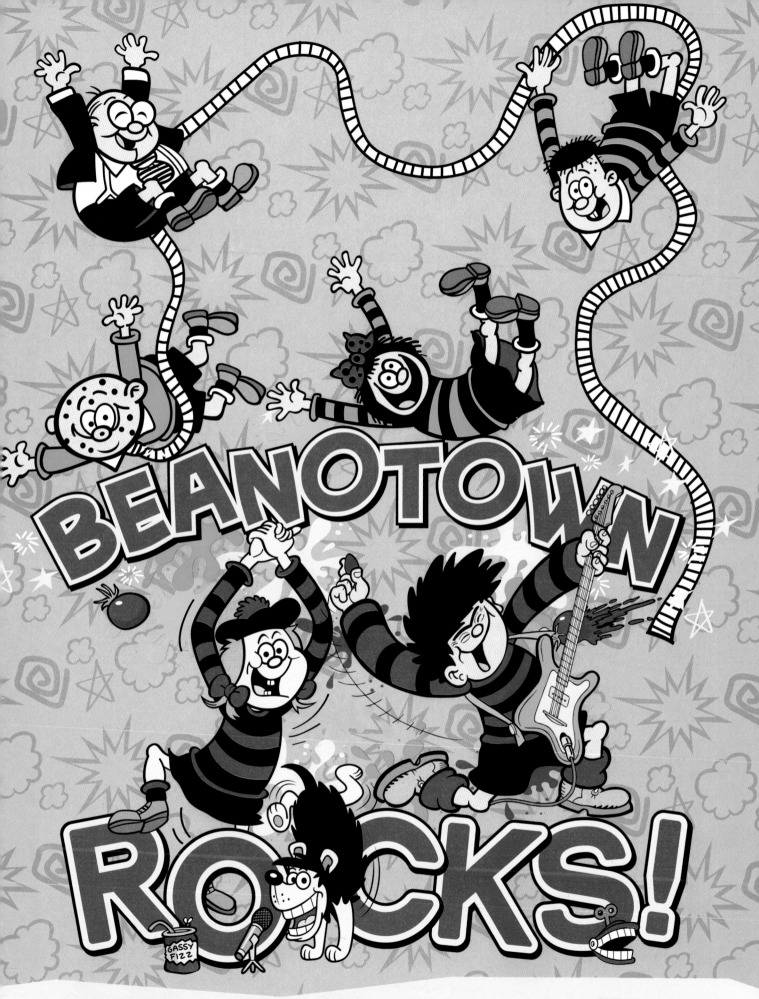

TEST YOUR STRENGTH

DUNK THE TEACHER

NIGEL PARKINSON. A.H.